...in the city

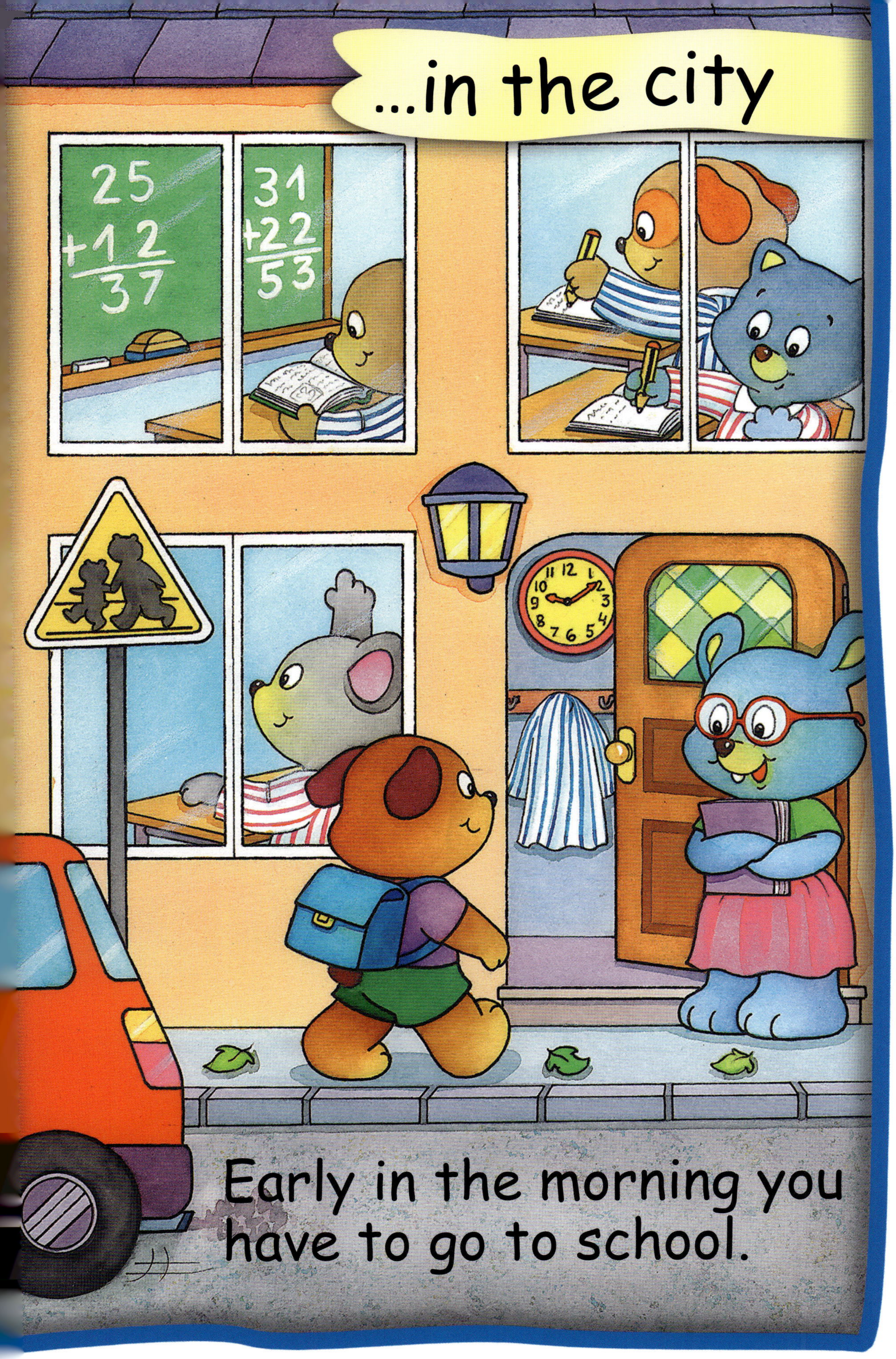

Early in the morning you have to go to school.

pencil

traffic sign

clock

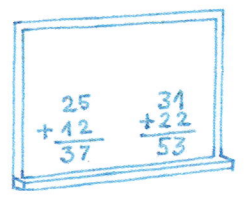
blackboard

schoolbag

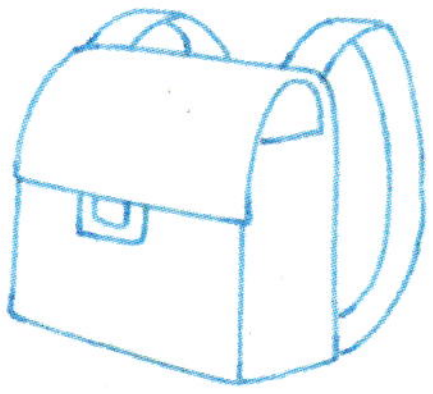

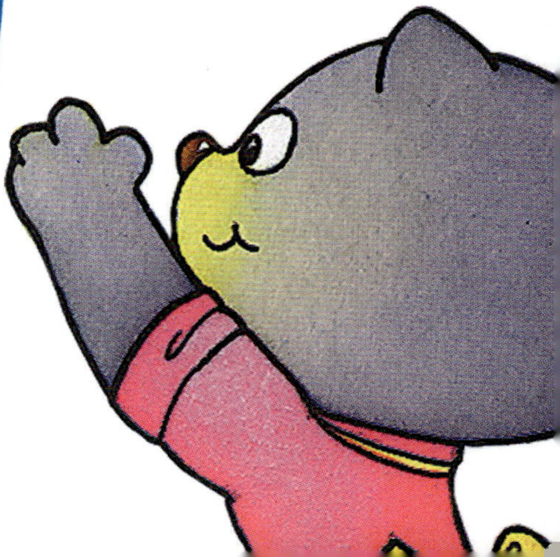

shopping basket

ladder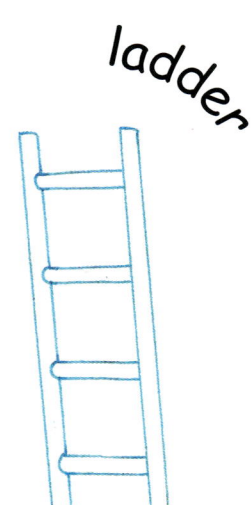

Many people live in cities and everyone goes to work.

can

shirt

container

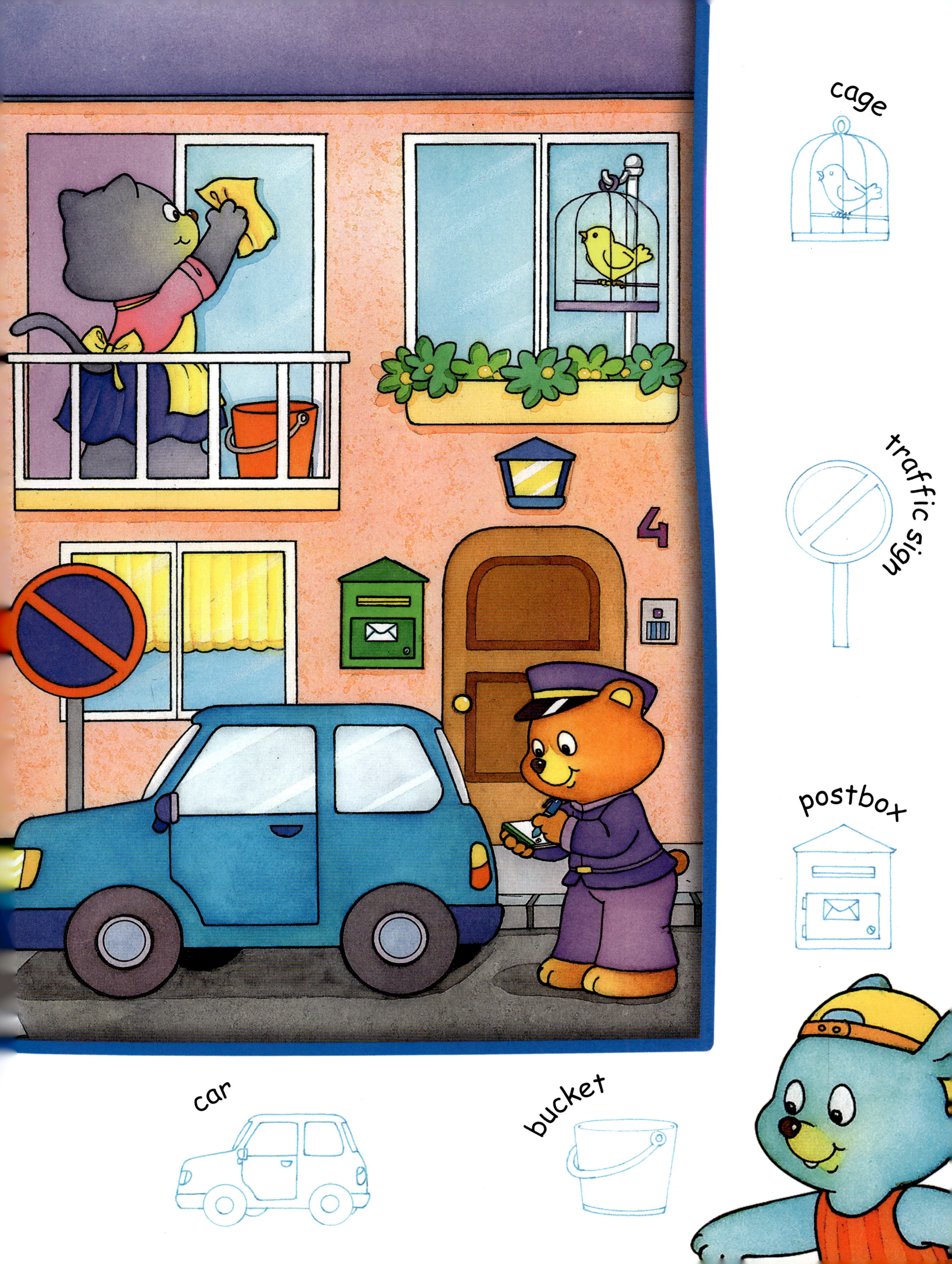

cage

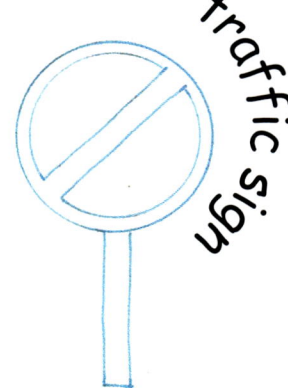
traffic sign

postbox

car

bucket

lawnmower

boat

skateboard

When the weather's fine, it's great to be in the park.

slide

bicycle

cassette

statue

camera

museum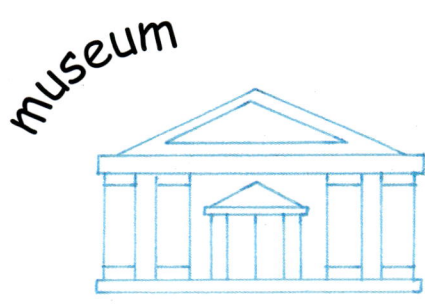

suitcase

syringe

Red Cross

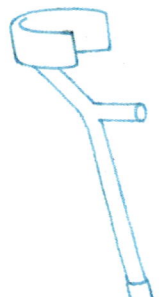
crutch

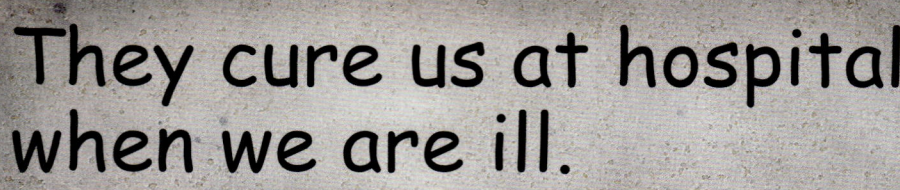
They cure us at hospital when we are ill.

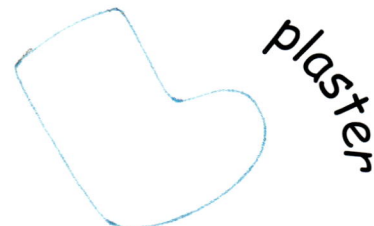
plaster

ambulance

pen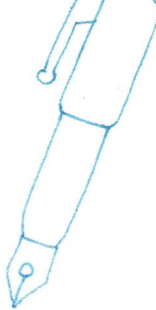

traffic lights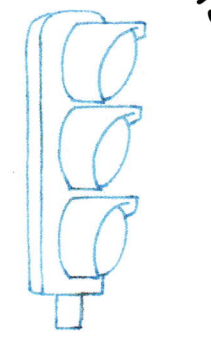

telephone

computer

motorbike

cake

broom
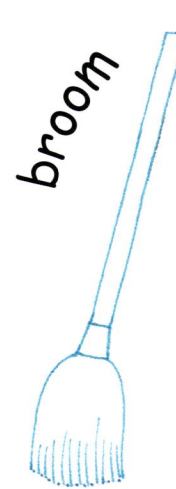

basket

The street is clean when the street sweeper cleans.

sports bag

glasses

...adventures!

Fish from the Pole sure is fresh!

coat

penguin

basket of fish

igloo

seal

water bottle

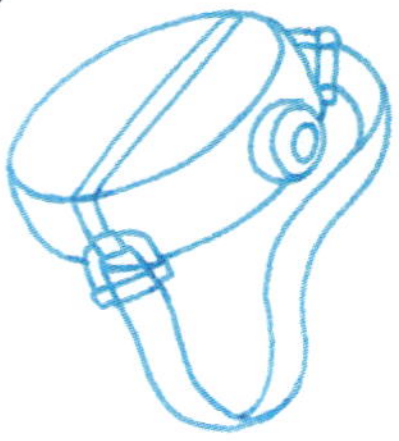

spade

salacot

tent

dromedary

Great surprises are found under the desert sands.

djellaba

pots

carpet

pyramid

scorpion

ice axe

fir tree

edelweiss

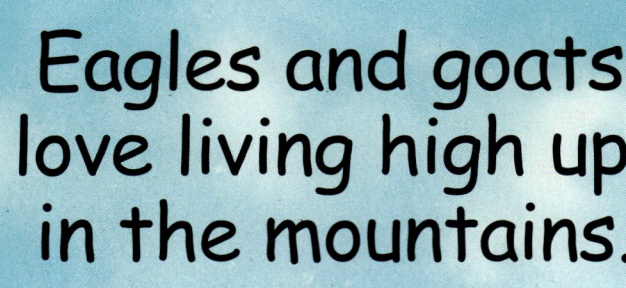
Eagles and goats love living high up in the mountains.

hut

eagle

flag

mountain goat

backpack

potholing helmet

binoculars

machete

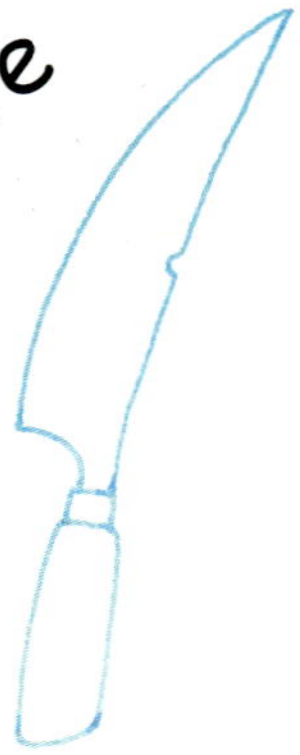

monkey

spear

snake

canoe

You have to be careful when walking through the jungle. Lots of dangerous animals live there.

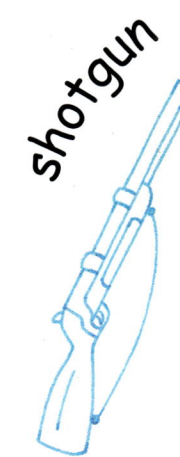
shotgun

toucan

oar

crocodile

hat

seahorse

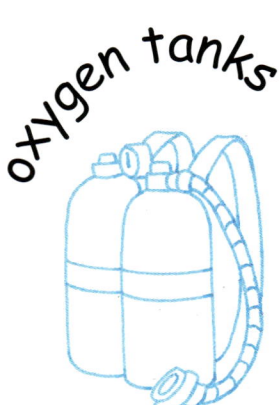
oxygen tanks

diving goggles

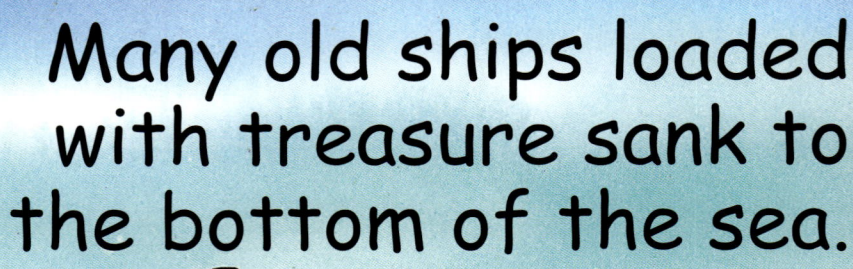
Many old ships loaded with treasure sank to the bottom of the sea.

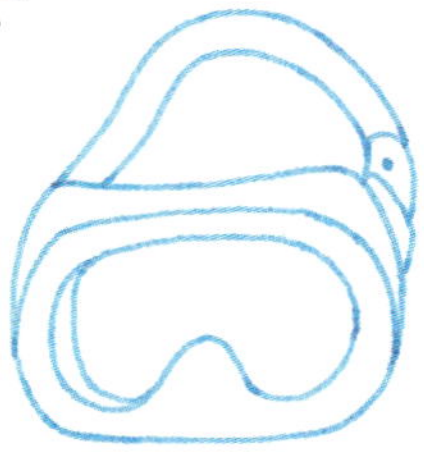

chest

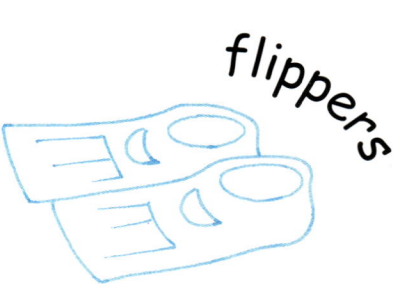
flippers

...travelling

Travelling by car is a pleasure.

scarecrow

ear of wheat

traffic sign

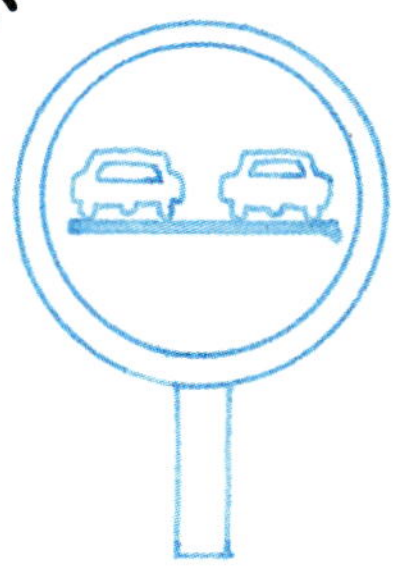

bicycle

convertible

sun

palm tree

starfish

sailing boat

pool raft
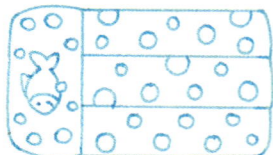

Water, sun, sand... and enjoy your holidays!

anchor

life jacket

sunshade

yacht

jet ski

balloon

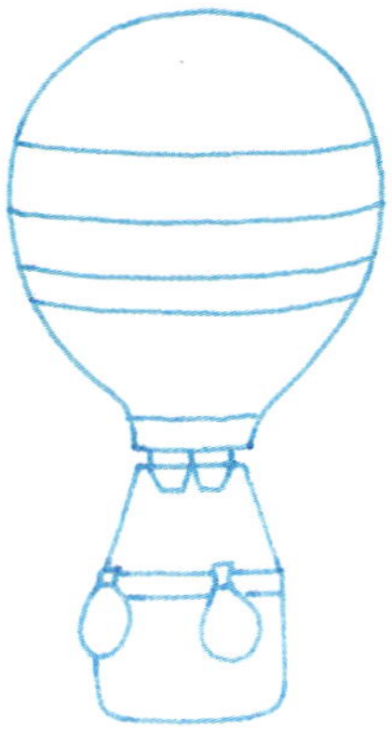

binoculars

postbox

Flying through the sky like a bird, how small everything looks from up above!

hang glider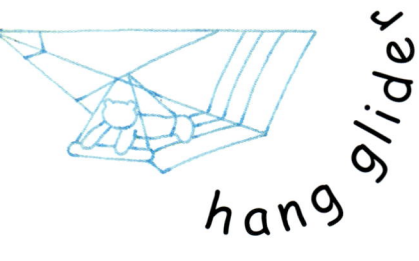

duck

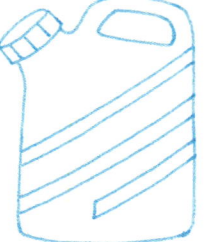
can of oil

sack

petrol pump

lorry

light aircraft

tree

windmill

teapot

caravan

barrier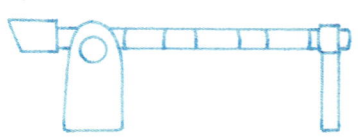

There goes the old train, as slow as a snail and puffing away!

traffic lights

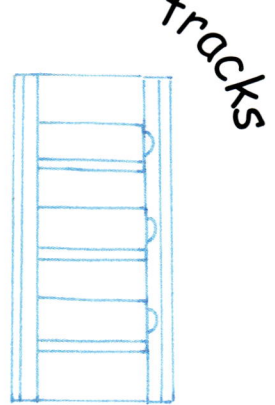
tracks

suitcase

tractor

train

lighthouse

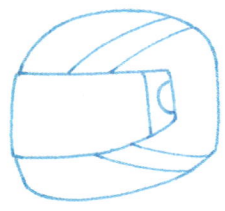
helmet

backpack

To travel by motorbike, you need a good helmet and a good pilot.

motorbike

cow